THIS BOOK BELONGS TO

MAZES ①

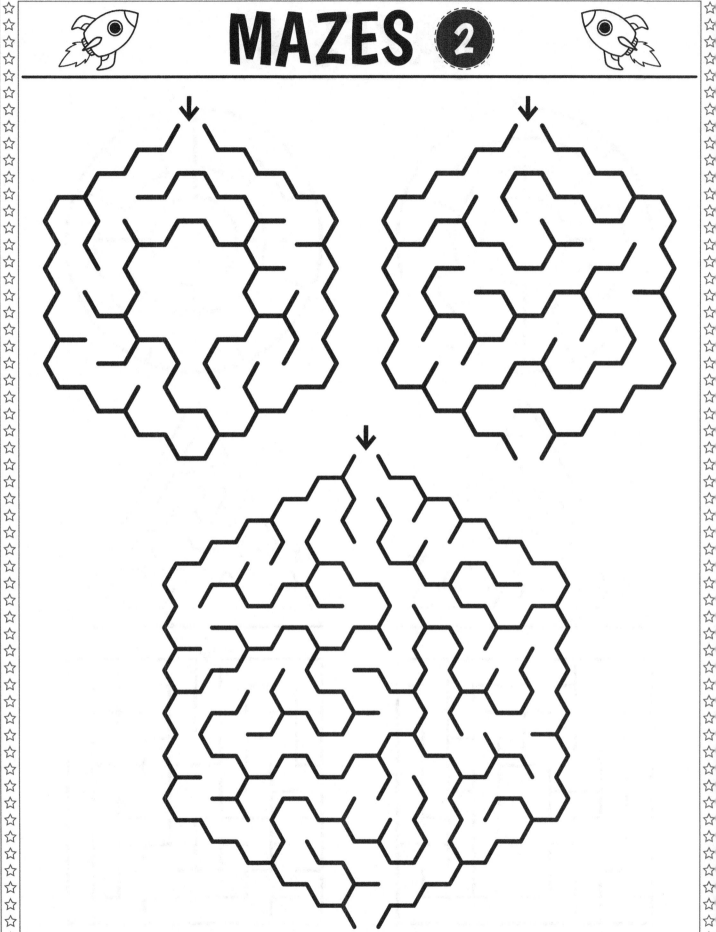

FIND THE WAY OUT OF THE MAZE

MAZES
3

FIND THE WAY INTO THE MAZE

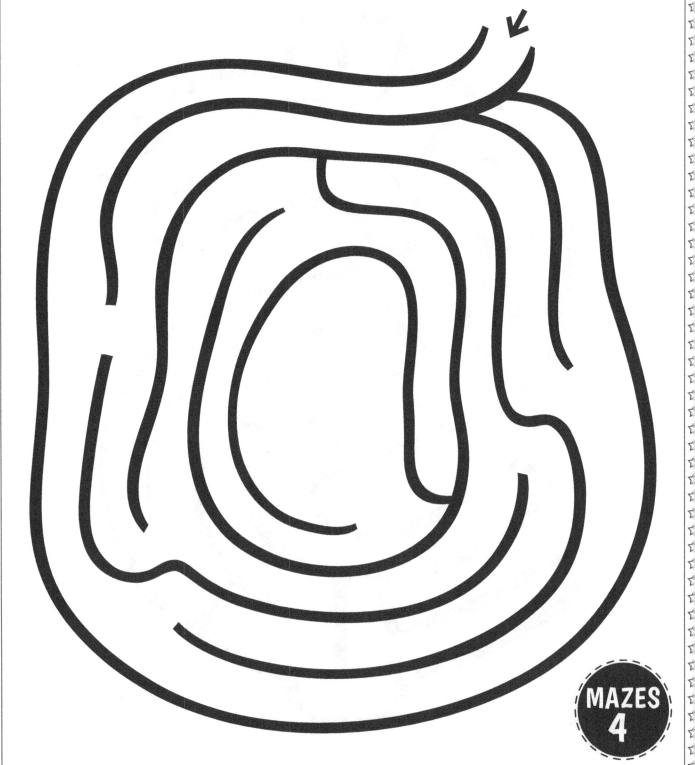

MAZES
4

FIND THE WAY OUT OF THE MAZE

MAZES
5

FIND THE WAY OUT OF THE MAZE

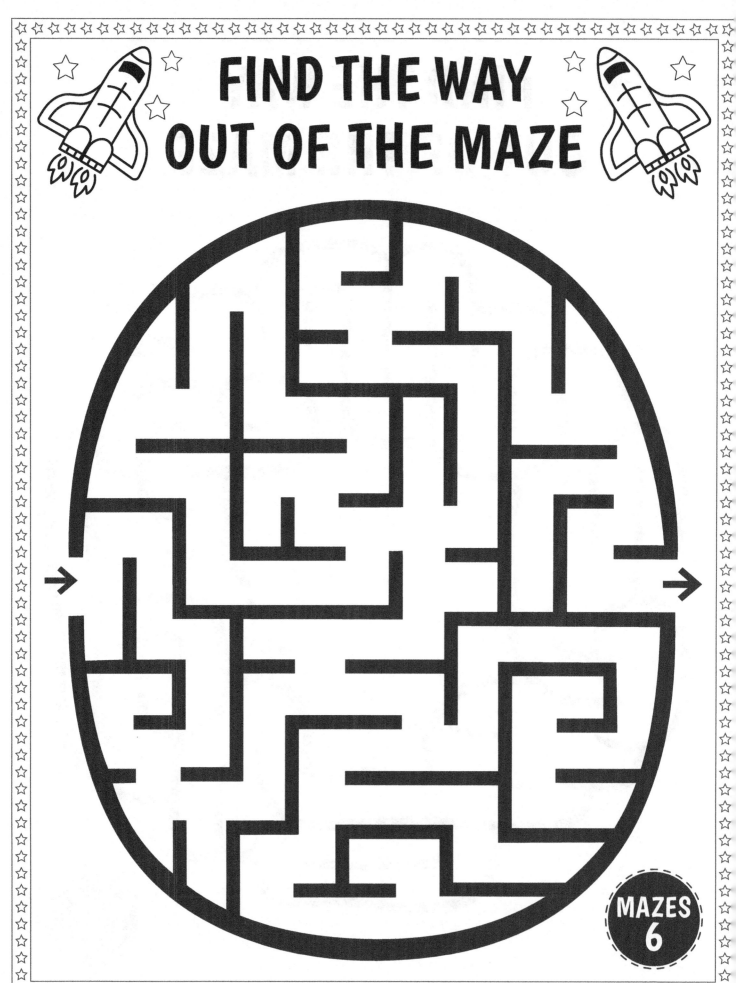

MAZES
6

FIND THE WAY
OUT OF THE MAZE

MAZES
7

FIND THE WAY
OUT OF THE MAZE

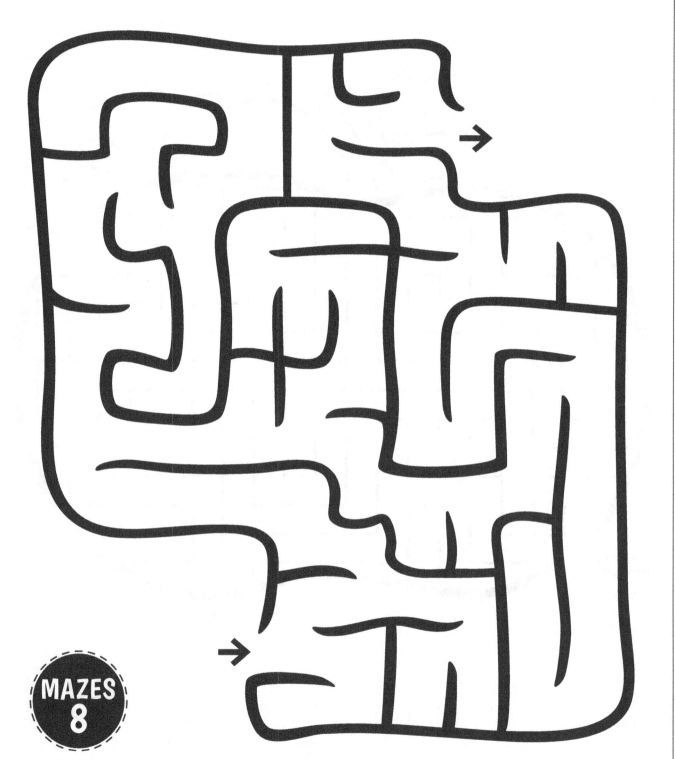

MAZES
8

FIND THE WAY OUT OF THE MAZE

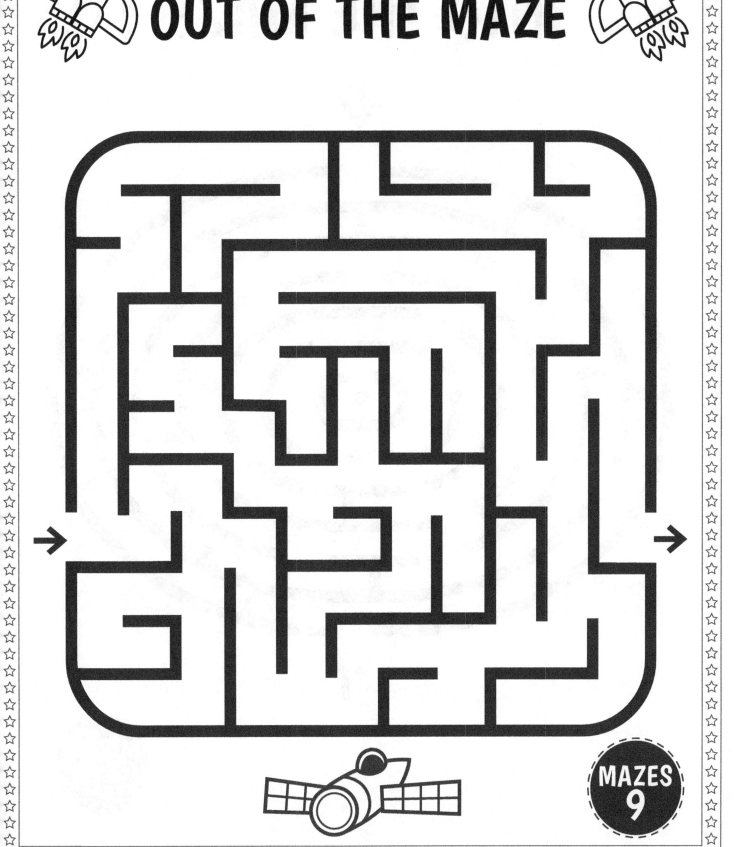

MAZES 9

FIND THE WAY INTO THE MAZE

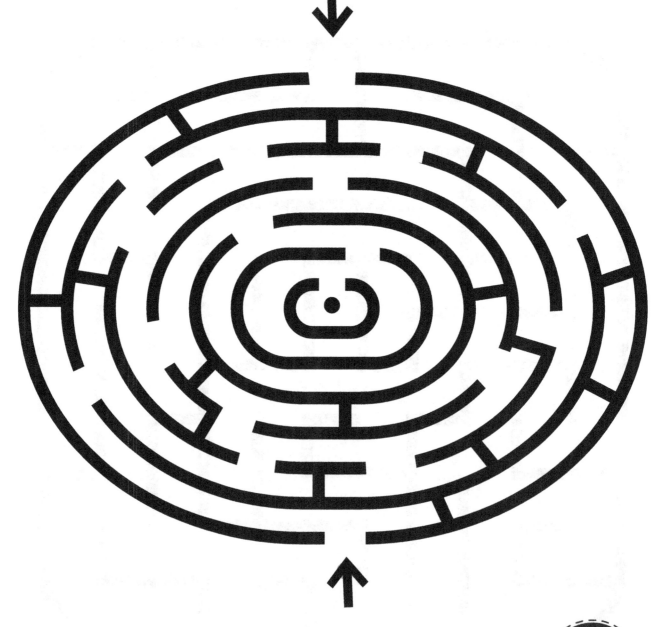

MAZES
10

FIND THE WAY INTO THE MAZE

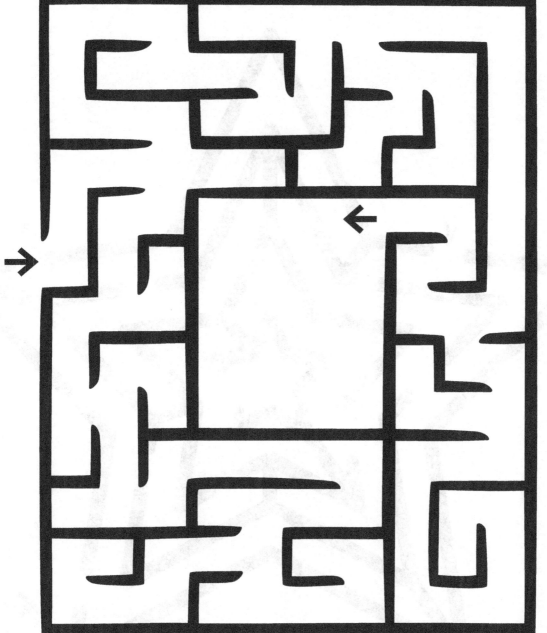

MAZES
11

FIND THE WAY
INTO THE MAZE

MAZES
12

FIND THE WAY OUT OF THE APPLE

FIND THE WAY OUT OF THE MAZE

MAZES
14

FIND THE WAY
OUT OF THE MAZE

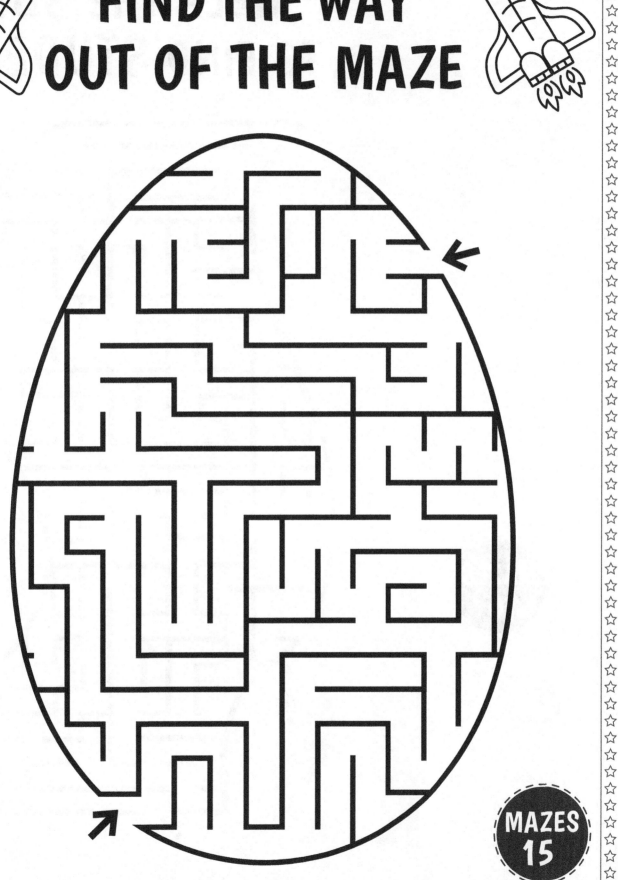

MAZES
15

HELP THE BUS TO FIND STUDENT

MAZES
16

FIND THE 2 WAY OUT OF THE MAZE

MAZES
17

FIND THE 2 WAY
INTO THE MAZE

MAZES
18

 # FIND THE WAY INTO THE MAZE

FIND THE WAY INTO THE MAZE

MAZES
20

FIND THE WAY INTO THE MAZE

FIND THE 3 WAY INTO THE MAZE

FIND THE WAY
OUT OF THE MAZE

FIND THE WAY
OUT OF THE MAZE

MAZES
24

FIND THE WAY INTO THE MAZE

MAZES
25

FIND THE WAY INTO THE MAZE

MAZES
26

FIND THE WAY OUT OF THE MAZE

MAZES
27

FIND THE WAY INTO THE CIRCLE

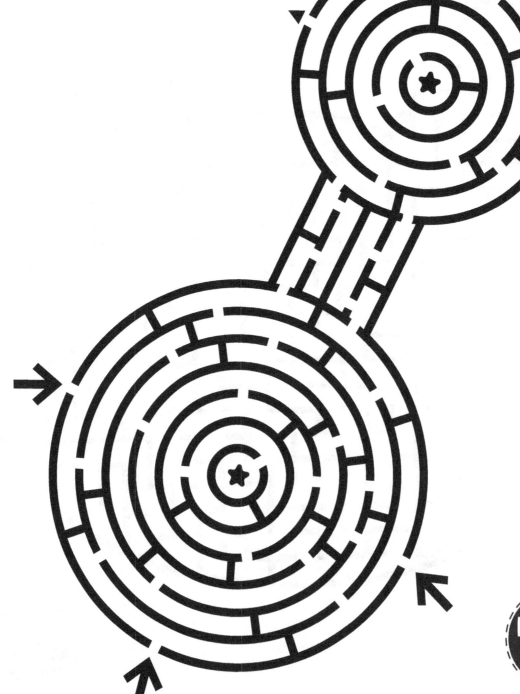

MAZES
28

FIND THE WAY
OUT OF THE MAZE

MAZES
29

FIND THE WAY INTO THE MAZE

MAZES
30

FIND THE WAY INTO THE MAZE

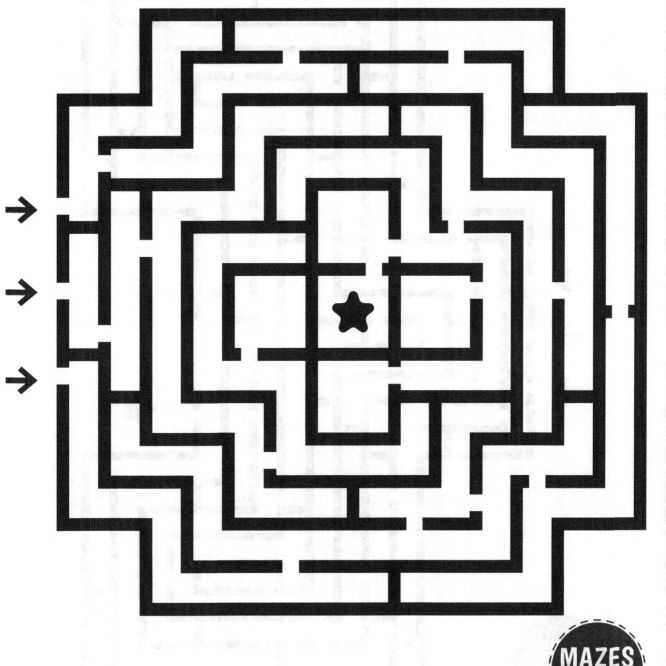

MAZES
31

FIND THE WAY OUT OF THE MAZE

FIND THE WAY
OUT OF THE MAZE

MAZES
33

FIND THE WAY INTO THE MAZE

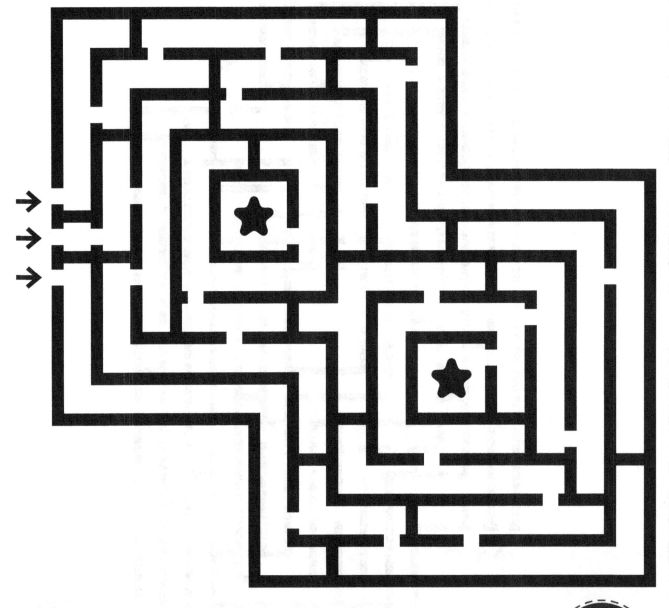

MAZES
34

FIND THE WAY
OUT OF THE MAZE

MAZES
35

HELP THE ASTRONAUT GET BACK TO HIS SHIP

HELP THE ASTRONAUT GET BACK TO EARTH

HELP THE ASTRONAUT
FIND URANUS

HELP THE KIDS TO SEE THE MOON

 # HELP THE ASTRONAUT TRAVEL TO GUPITER!

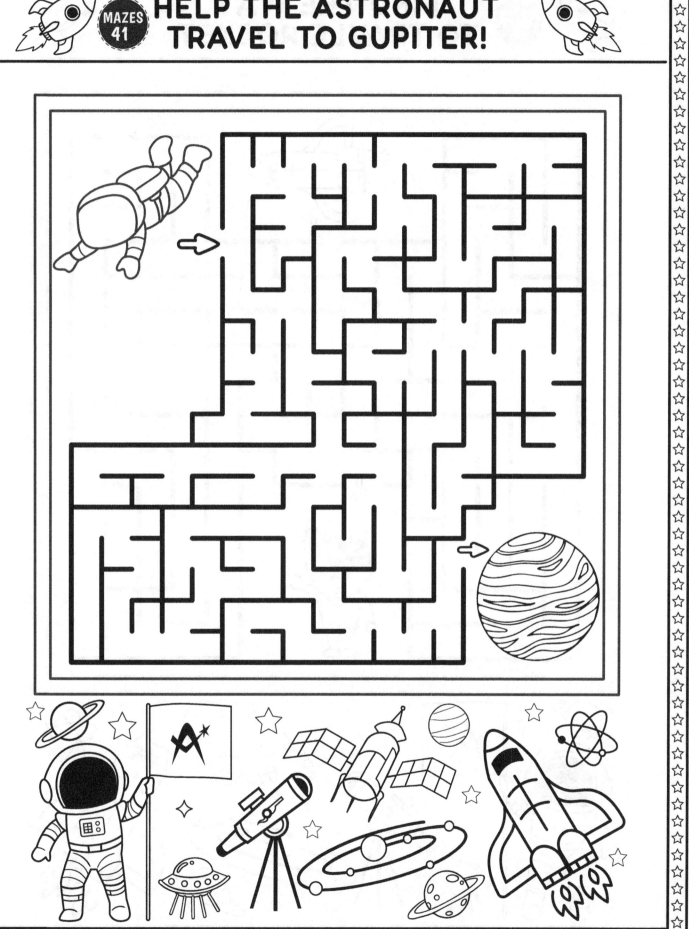

FIND THE WAY
TO TRAVLE ROCKET

HELP THE ASTRONAUT TRAVEL TO GALAXY

SHAPE MAZE

Start

End

ROBOT

SHAPE MAZE

Start

End

ROCKET

SHAPE MAZE

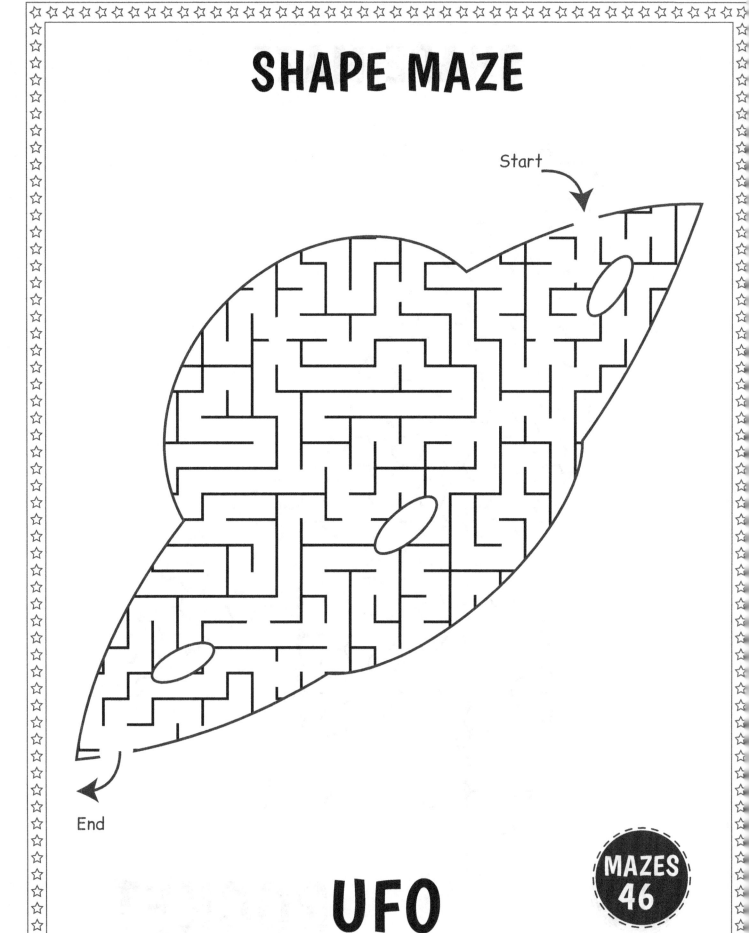

Start

End

UFO

SHAPE MAZE

Start

End

STAR

SHAPE MAZE

Start

End

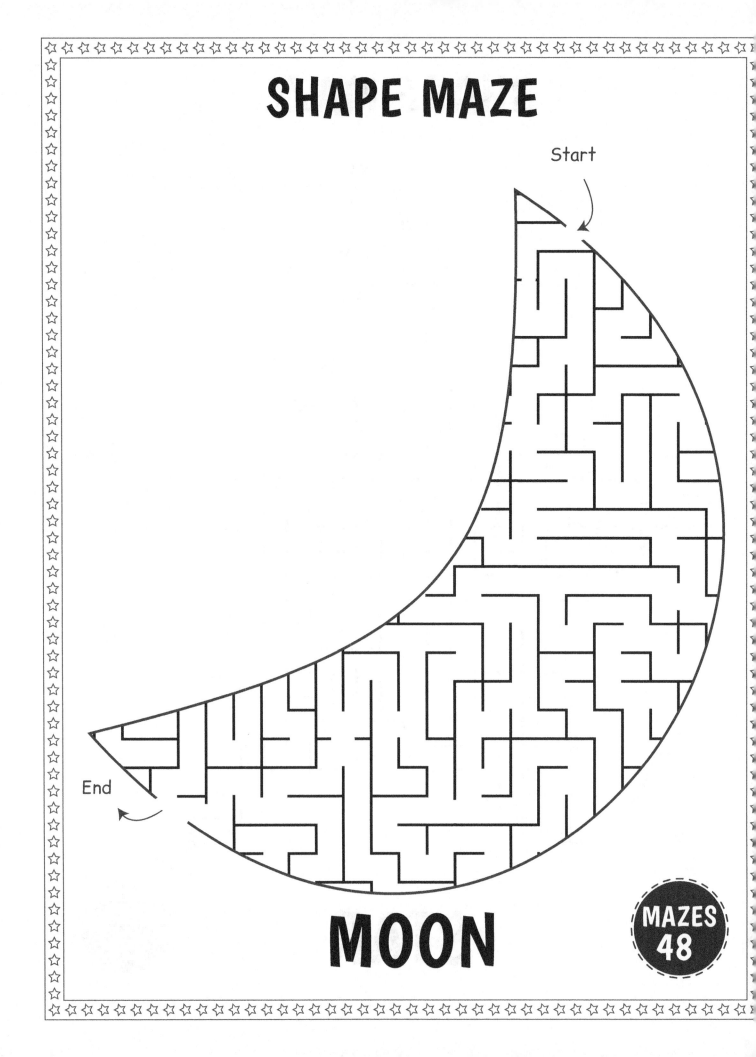

MOON

MAZES
48

MAZE

ICECREAM

MAZE

MAZES 50

ICE CREAM BALLS

WHICH ROBOT WILL BE CHARGED ?

MAZES 51

FINISH

Let's Help The Astronaut Get Back to the Spaceship

MAZES 52

MAZES 53

Let's Help The Rabbit to Find The Carrots

HELP THE SQUIRREL TO FIND NUTS

MAZES 54

MAZES
55

HELP THE VEGAN TO FIND SALAD

MAZES 56

MAZES
57

FIND THE WAY GOING TO SCHOOL

MAZES 58

HELP THE LITTLE BUNNY TO FIND MUM

MAZES
59

HELP THE LITTLE HEDGEHOG FIND THE WAY TO THE APPLE

MAZES
60

HELP THE LITTLE BUNNY TO FIND HOME

MAZES
61

HELP THE MONKEY TO FIND BANANAS

MAZES
62

MISSING BOOT

LET'S HELP "MOUSTACHE" THE CAT TO FIND HIS BOOT

MAZES
63

HELP THE LEMUR COLLECT ALL PINEAPPLES

MAZES 64

HELP THE UNICORN TO FIND A WAY!

MAZES
65

MAZES
66

HELP THE LITTLE BEES
TO FIND THEIR FLOWERS

HELP THE ASTRONAUT

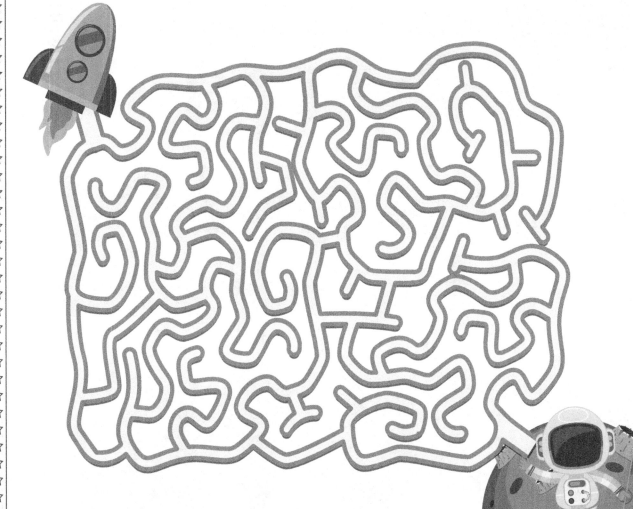

GET BACK TO HIS SHIP

FINISH

START

MAZES
68

BRING THE BEAR TO HONEY

HELP THE BUNNY FIND THE EASTER EGGS

MAZES
70

A   B   C

MAZES
71

MAZES
72

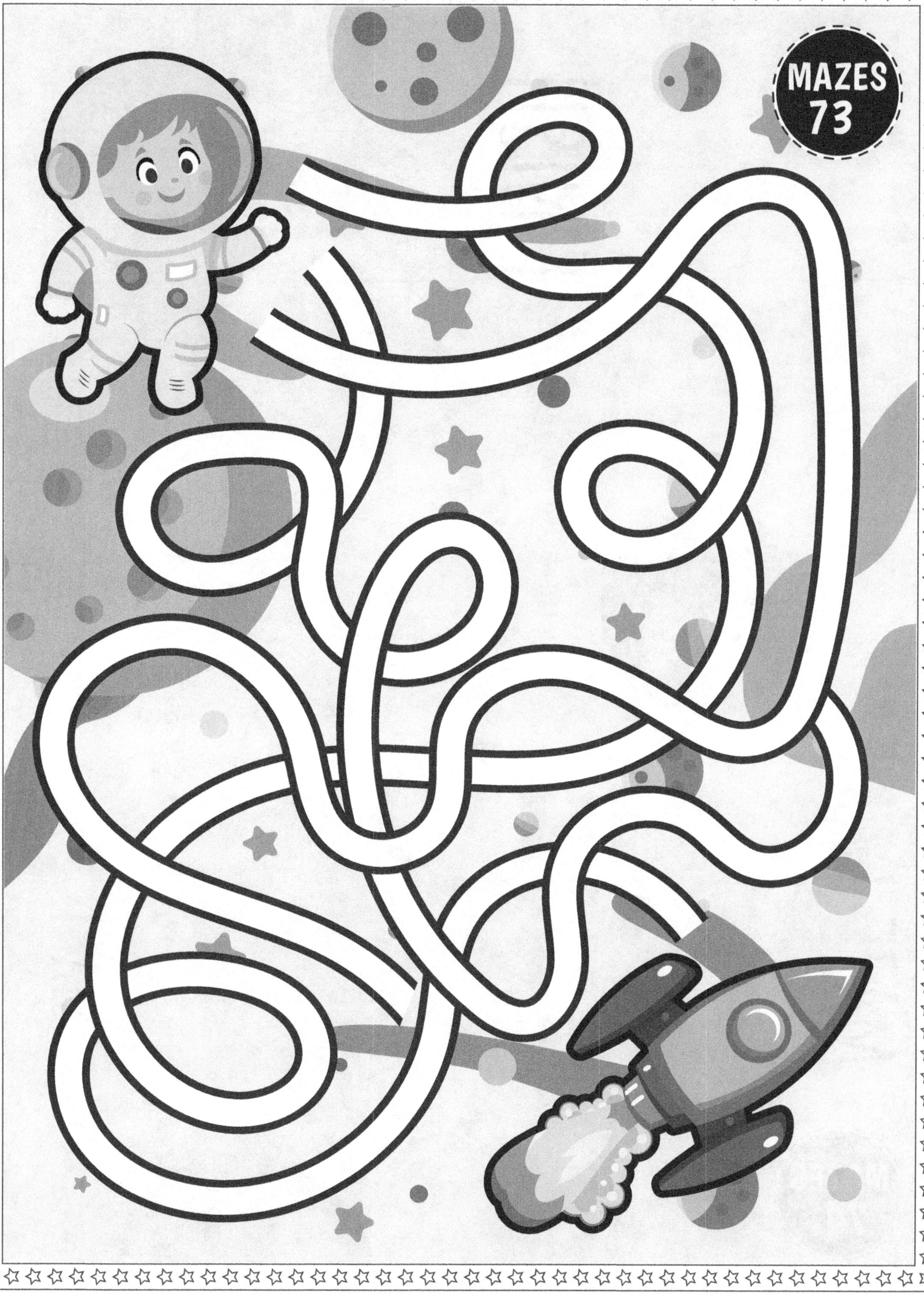
MAZES
73

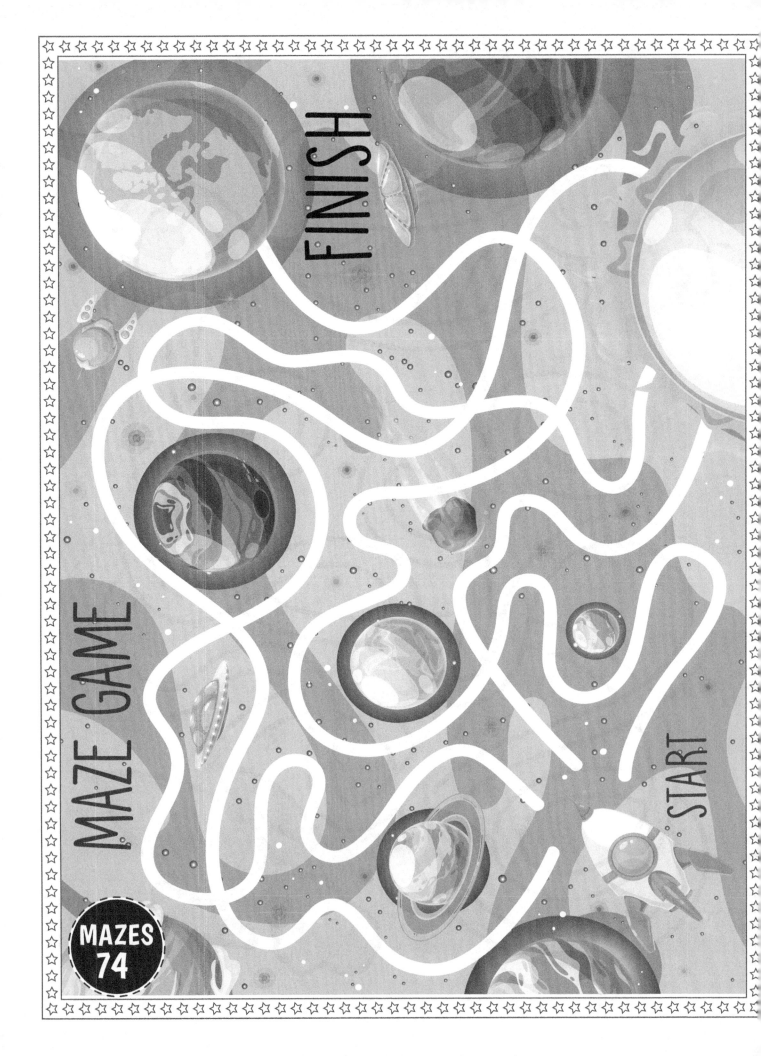

MAZES
75

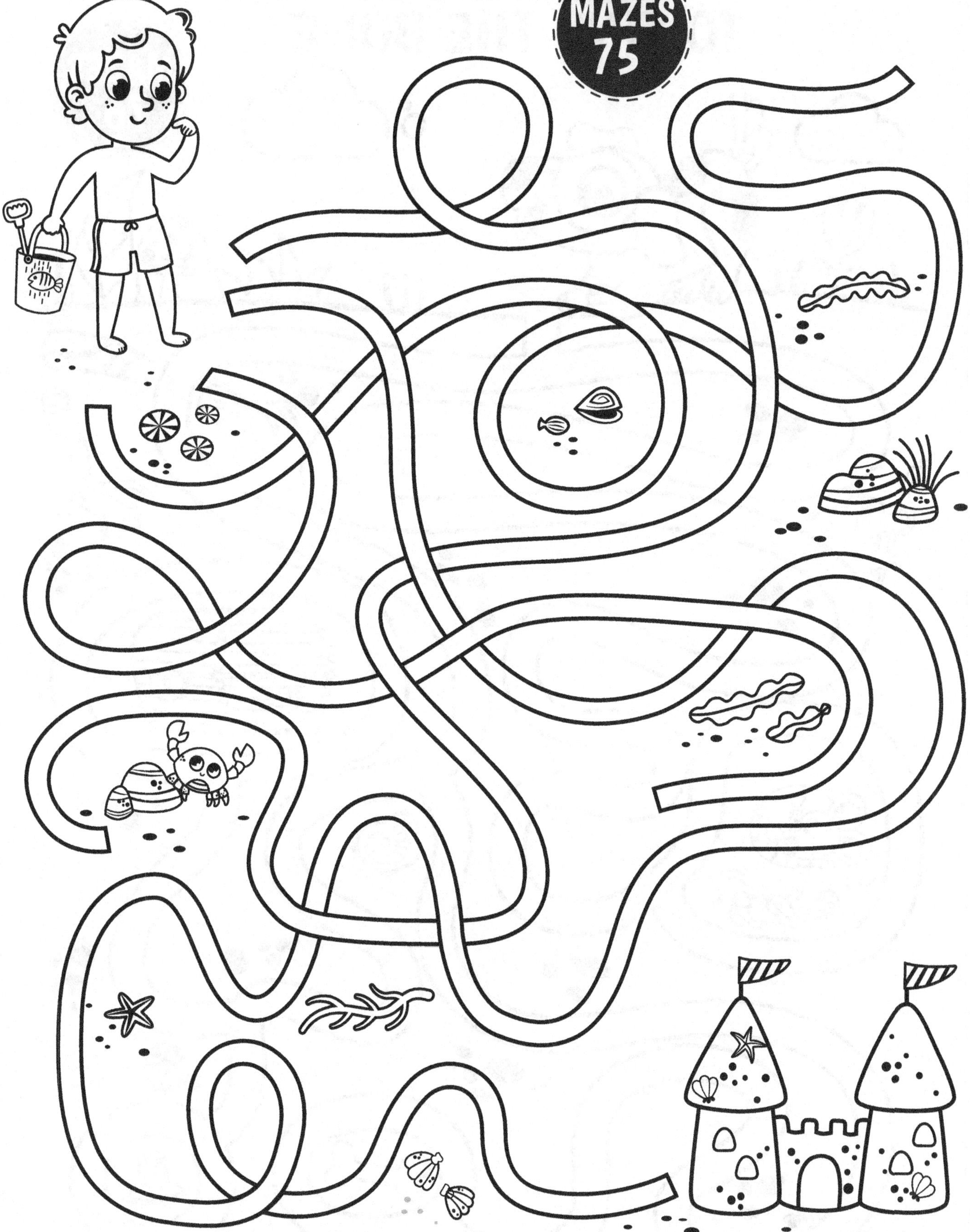

HELP THE DOG TO FIND THE BONE

MAZES
76

HELP THE ASTRONAUT
FIND THE WAY TO THE ROCKET

MAZES
77

HELP THE SCUBA DIVER
TO FIND THE BOAT

HELP THE ASTRONAUT TO REACH THE MOON

MAZES
79

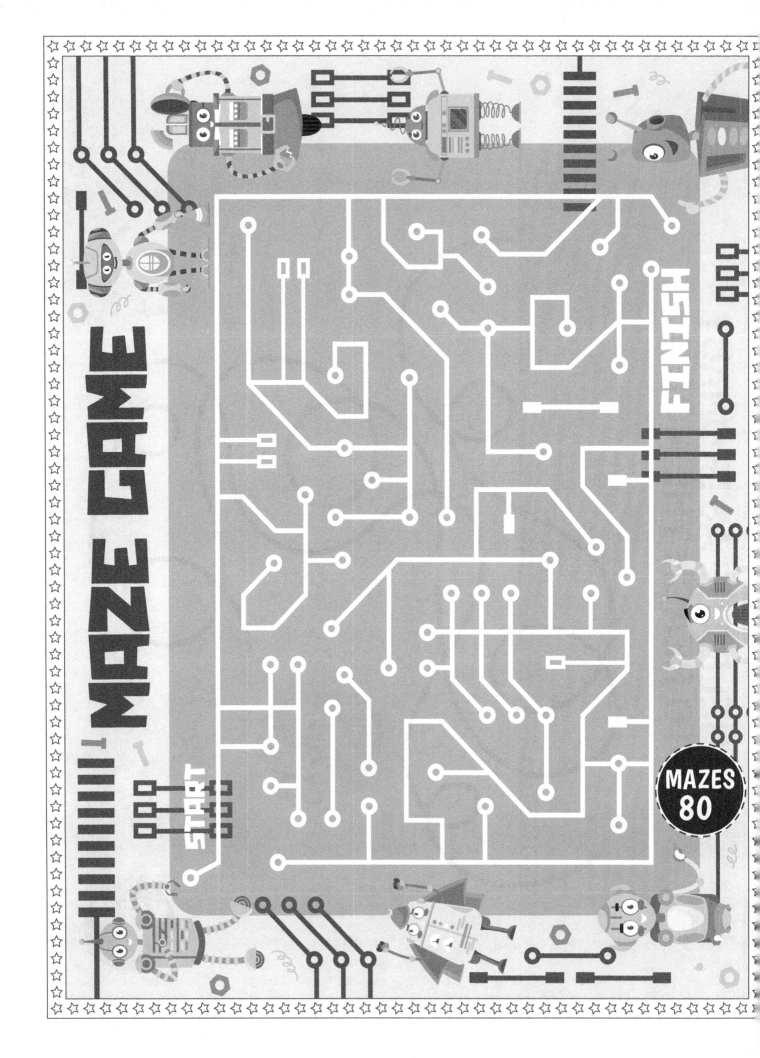

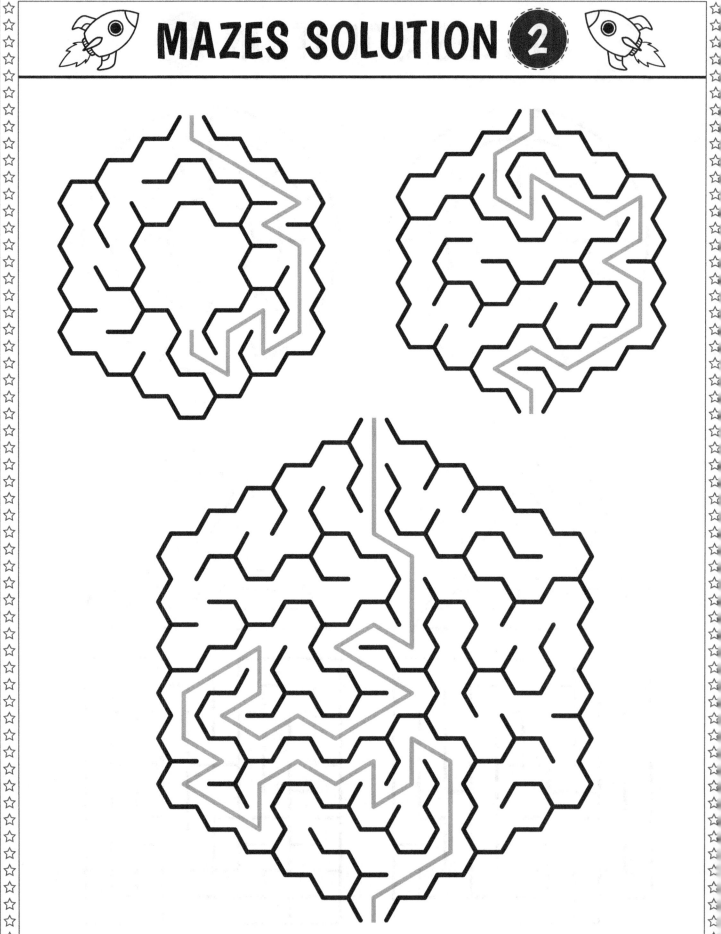

MAZES SOLUTION

FIND THE WAY OUT OF THE MAZE

MAZES
3

FIND THE WAY INTO THE MAZE

MAZES
4

FIND THE WAY OUT OF THE MAZE

MAZES
5

FIND THE WAY OUT OF THE MAZE

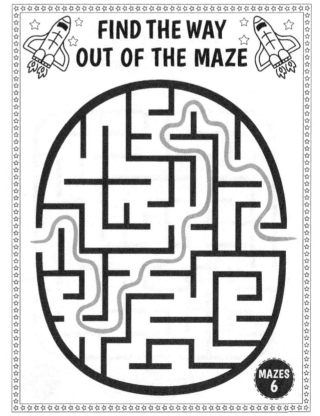

MAZES
6

MAZES SOLUTION

FIND THE WAY OUT OF THE MAZE

MAZES 7

FIND THE WAY OUT OF THE MAZE

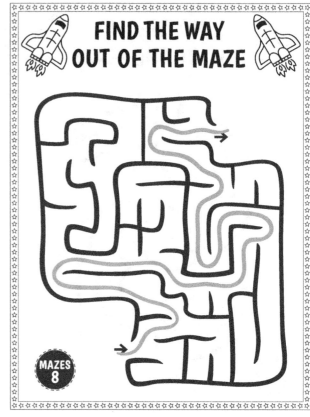

MAZES 8

FIND THE WAY OUT OF THE MAZE

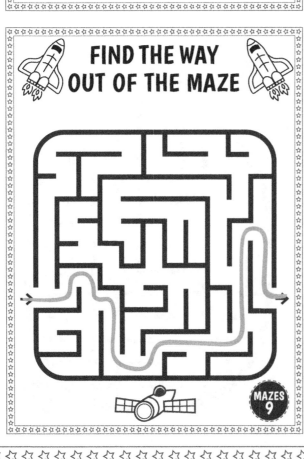

MAZES 9

FIND THE WAY INTO THE MAZE

MAZES 10

MAZES SOLUTION

FIND THE WAY INTO THE MAZE

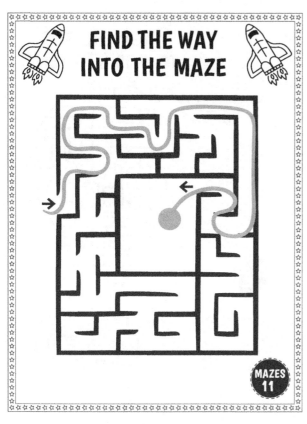

MAZES 11

FIND THE WAY INTO THE MAZE

A

B

MAZES 12

FIND THE WAY OUT OF THE APPLE

MAZES 13

FIND THE WAY OUT OF THE MAZE

MAZES 14

MAZES SOLUTION

FIND THE WAY OUT OF THE MAZE

MAZES 15

HELP THE BUS TO FIND STUDENT

MAZES 16

FIND THE 2 WAY OUT OF THE MAZE

A

B

MAZES 17

FIND THE 2 WAY INTO THE MAZE

C

A

B

MAZES 18

MAZES SOLUTION

FIND THE WAY INTO THE MAZE

MAZES 19

FIND THE WAY INTO THE MAZE

MAZES 20

FIND THE WAY INTO THE MAZE

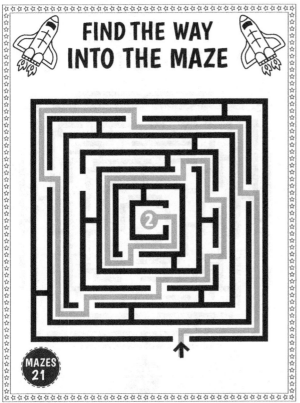

MAZES 21

FIND THE 3 WAY INTO THE MAZE

MAZES 22

MAZES SOLUTION

FIND THE WAY OUT OF THE MAZE

MAZES 23

FIND THE WAY OUT OF THE MAZE

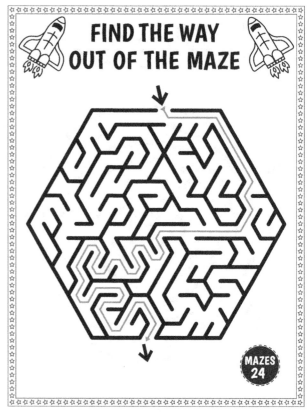

MAZES 24

FIND THE WAY INTO THE MAZE

MAZES 25

FIND THE WAY INTO THE MAZE

MAZES 26

MAZES SOLUTION

FIND THE WAY OUT OF THE MAZE

MAZES 27

FIND THE WAY INTO THE CIRCLE

MAZES 28

FIND THE WAY OUT OF THE MAZE

MAZES 29

FIND THE WAY INTO THE MAZE

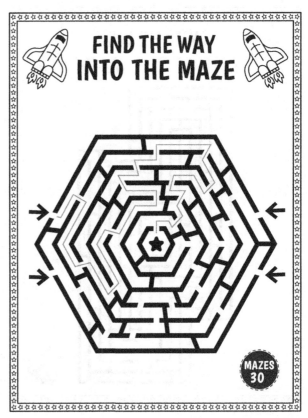

MAZES 30

MAZES SOLUTION

FIND THE WAY INTO THE MAZE

MAZES
31

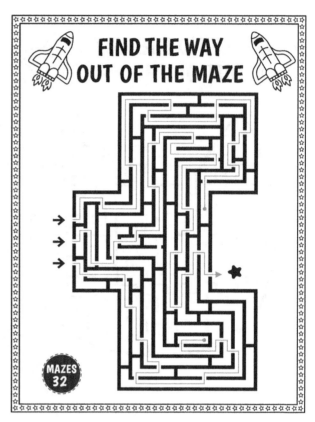

FIND THE WAY OUT OF THE MAZE

MAZES
32

FIND THE WAY OUT OF THE MAZE

MAZES
33

FIND THE WAY INTO THE MAZE

MAZES
34

MAZES SOLUTION

FIND THE WAY OUT OF THE MAZE

MAZES 35

HELP THE ASTRONAUT GET BACK TO HIS SHIP

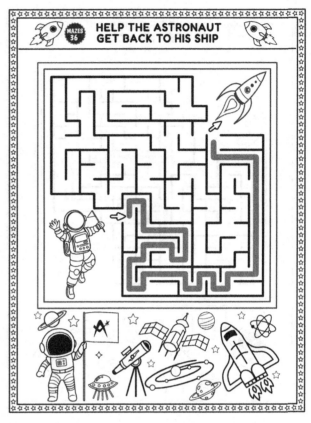

HELP THE ASTRONAUT GET BACK TO EARTH

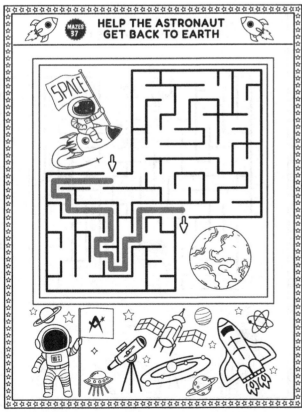

HELP THE ASTRONAUT FIND URANUS

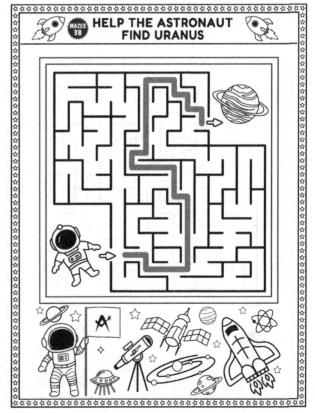

MAZES SOLUTION

HELP THE KIDS TO SEE THE MOON

HELP THE ASTRONAUT TO REACH THE MOON

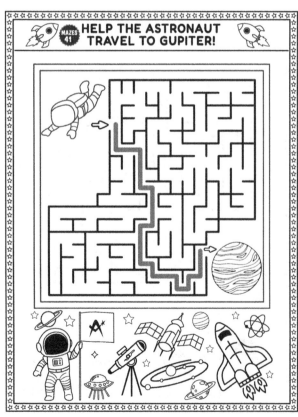

HELP THE ASTRONAUT TRAVEL TO GUPITER!

FIND THE WAY TO TRAVLE ROCKET

MAZES SOLUTION

HELP THE ASTRONAUT TRAVEL TO GALAXY

MAZES 43

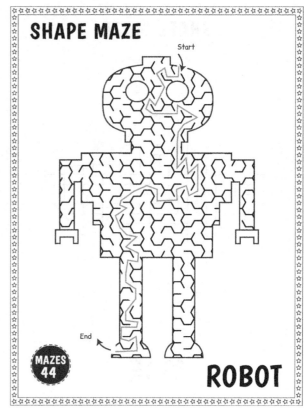

SHAPE MAZE

Start

End

MAZES 44

ROBOT

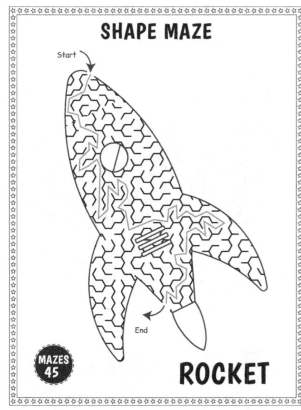

SHAPE MAZE

Start

End

MAZES 45

ROCKET

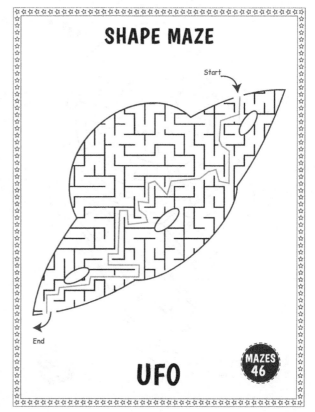

SHAPE MAZE

Start

End

UFO

MAZES 46

MAZES SOLUTION

SHAPE MAZE

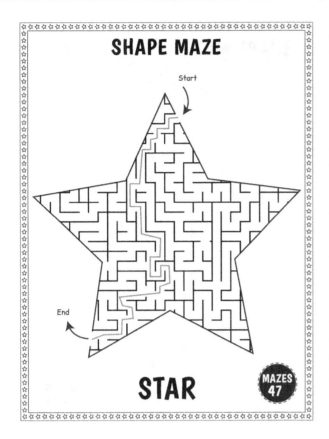

Start

End

STAR

MAZES
47

SHAPE MAZE

Start

End

MOON

MAZES
48

MAZE

ICECREAM

MAZES
49

MAZE

MAZES
50

ICE CREAM BALLS

MAZES SOLUTION

MAZES
55

HELP THE VEGAN TO FIND SALAD

MAZES
56

MAZES
57

FIND THE WAY GOING TO SCHOOL

MAZES
58

MAZES SOLUTION

HELP THE LITTLE BUNNY TO FIND MUM

HELP THE LITTLE HEDGEHOG FIND THE WAY TO THE APPLE

MAZES 60

HELP THE LITTLE BUNNY TO FIND HOME

MAZES 61

HELP THE MONKEY TO FIND BANANAS

MAZES 62

MAZES SOLUTION

MISSING BOOT

LET'S HELP "MOUSTACHE" THE CAT TO FIND HIS BOOT

MAZES 63

HELP THE LEMUR COLLECT ALL PINEAPPLES

MAZES 64

HELP THE UNICORN TO FIND A WAY!

MAZES 65

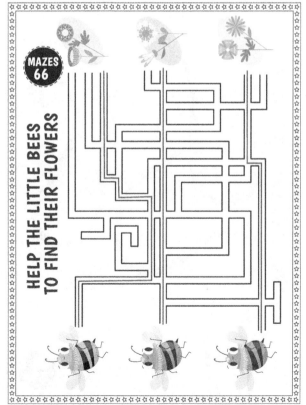

HELP THE LITTLE BEES TO FIND THEIR FLOWERS

MAZES 66

MAZES SOLUTION

HELP THE ASTRONAUT

MAZES 67

GET BACK TO HIS SHIP

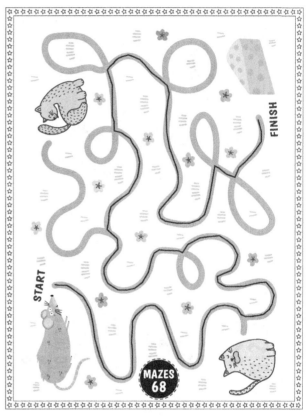

START

FINISH

MAZES 68

BRING THE BEAR TO HONEY

MAZES 69

HELP THE BUNNY FIND THE EASTER EGGS

MAZES 70

MAZES SOLUTION

MAZES
71

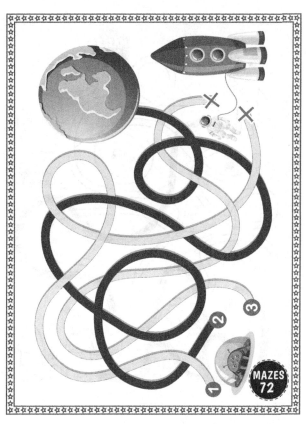

MAZES
72

MAZES
73

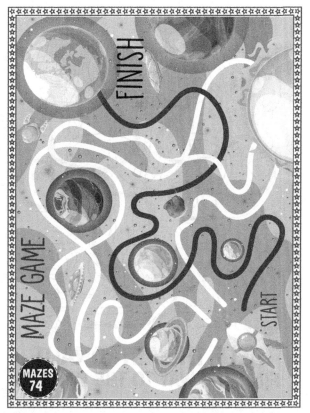

MAZE GAME

FINISH

START

MAZES
74

MAZES SOLUTION

MAZES 75

HELP THE DOG TO FIND THE BONE

MAZES 76

MAZES 77

HELP THE ASTRONAUT
FIND THE WAY TO THE ROCKET

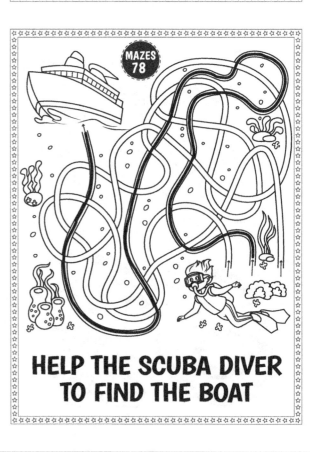

MAZES 78

HELP THE SCUBA DIVER TO FIND THE BOAT

Made in the USA
Monee, IL
06 March 2024

54582949R00057